ROSS RICHIE CEO & Founder • **MARK SMYLIE** Founder of Archaia • **MATT GAGNON** Editor-in-Chief • **FILIP SABLIK** VP of Publishing & Marketing • **STEPHEN CHRISTY** VP of Development
LANCE KREITER VP of Licensing & Merchandising • **PHIL BARBARO** VP of Finance • **BRYCE CARLSON** Managing Editor • **MEL CAYLO** Marketing Manager • **SCOTT NEWMAN** Production Design Manager
IRENE BRADISH Operations Manager • **CHRISTINE DINH** Brand Communications Manager • **DAFNA PLEBAN** Editor • **SHANNON WATTERS** Editor • **ERIC HARBURN** Editor • **REBECCA TAYLOR** Editor
IAN BRILL Editor • **CHRIS ROSA** Assistant Editor • **ALEX GALER** Assistant Editor • **WHITNEY LEOPARD** Assistant Editor • **JASMINE AMIRI** Assistant Editor • **CAMERON CHITTOCK** Assistant Editor
KELSEY DIETERICH Production Designer • **EMI YONEMURA BROWN** Production Designer • **DEVIN FUNCHES** E-Commerce & Inventory Coordinator • **ANDY LIEGL** Event Coordinator • **BRIANNA HART** Executive Assistant
AARON FERRARA Operations Assistant • **JOSÉ MEZA** Sales Assistant • **MICHELLE ANKLEY** Sales Assistant • **ELIZABETH LOUGHRIDGE** Accounting Assistant • **STEPHANIE HOCUTT** PR Assistant

ADVENTURE TIME Volume Four Scholastic Edition, June 2014. Published by KaBOOM!, a division of Boom Entertainment, Inc. ADVENTURE TIME, CARTOON
NETWORK, the logos, and all related characters and elements are trademarks of and © Cartoon Network. (S14) Originally published in single magazine form as
ADVENTURE TIME 15-19. © Cartoon Network. (S13) All rights reserved. KaBOOM!™ and the KaBOOM! logo are trademarks of Boom Entertainment, Inc., registered in
various countries and categories. All characters, events, and institutions depicted herein are fictional. Any similarity between any of the names, characters, persons, events,
and/or institutions in this publication to actual names, characters, and persons, whether living or dead, events, and/or institutions is unintended and purely coincidental.
KaBOOM! does not read or accept unsolicited submissions of ideas, stories, or artwork.

For information regarding the CPSIA on this printed material, call: (203) 595-3636 and provide reference RICH# – 561971. A catalog record of this book is available from
OCLC and from the KaBOOM! website, www.kaboom-studios.com, on the Librarians Page.

BOOM! Studios, 5670 Wilshire Boulevard, Suite 450, Los Angeles, CA 90036-5679. Printed in USA. First Printing. ISBN: 978-1-60886-475-1, eISBN: 978-1-61398-329-4

CREATED BY
Pendleton Ward

WRITTEN BY
Ryan North

ILLUSTRATED BY
Shelli Paroline & Braden Lamb

ADDITIONAL COLORS BY
Lisa Moore

LETTERS BY
Steve Wands

COVER BY
Drew Weing

ASSISTANT EDITOR
Whitney Leopard

EDITOR
Shannon Watters

TRADE DESIGN
**Stephanie Gonzaga
& Hannah Nance Partlow**

With special thanks to
Marisa Marionakis, Rick Blanco, Curtis Lelash, Laurie Halal-Ono, Keith
Mack, Kelly Crews and the wonderful folks at Cartoon Network.

Sandwiches do not work that way BMO. I've tried. Oh how I've tried.

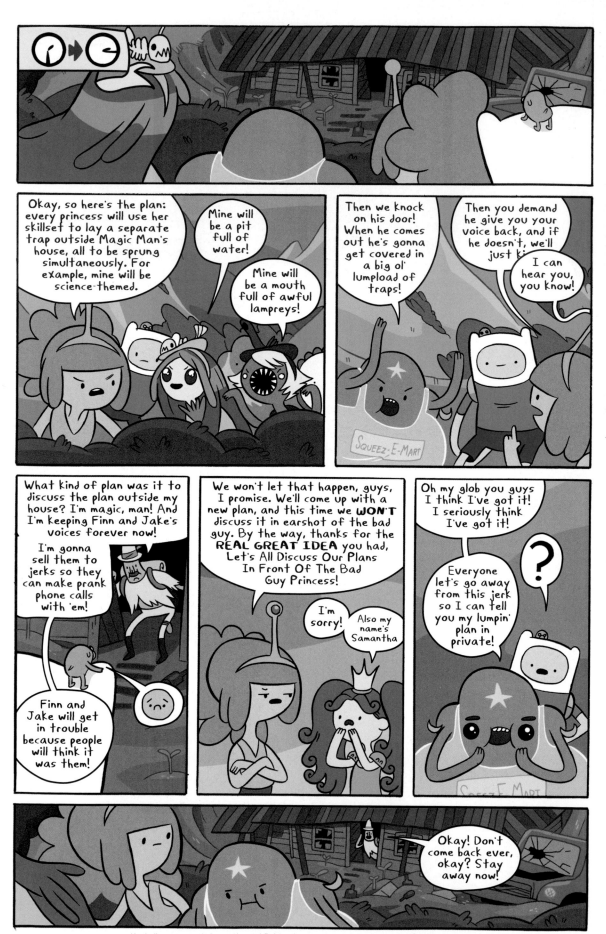

Okay, so here's the plan: every princess will use her skillset to lay a separate trap outside Magic Man's house, all to be sprung simultaneously. For example, mine will be science-themed.

Mine will be a pit full of water!

Mine will be a mouth full of awful lampreys!

Then we knock on his door! When he comes out he's gonna get covered in a big ol' lumpload of traps!

Then you demand he give you your voice back, and if he doesn't, we'll just ki—

I can hear you, you know!

SQUEEZ-E-MART

What kind of plan was it to discuss the plan outside my house? I'm magic, man! And I'm keeping Finn and Jake's voices forever now!

I'm gonna sell them to jerks so they can make prank phone calls with 'em!

Finn and Jake will get in trouble because people will think it was them!

We won't let that happen, guys, I promise. We'll come up with a new plan, and this time we **WON'T** discuss it in earshot of the bad guy. By the way, thanks for the **REAL GREAT IDEA** you had, Let's All Discuss Our Plans In Front Of The Bad Guy Princess!

I'm sorry!

Also my name's Samantha

Oh my glob you guys I think I've got it! I seriously think I've got it!

Everyone let's go away from this jerk so I can tell you my lumpin' plan in private!

?

Okay! Don't come back ever, okay? Stay away now!

SQEEZ E MART

Yes hello my name is Samantha and I do not appreciate being the victim of most sarcasms

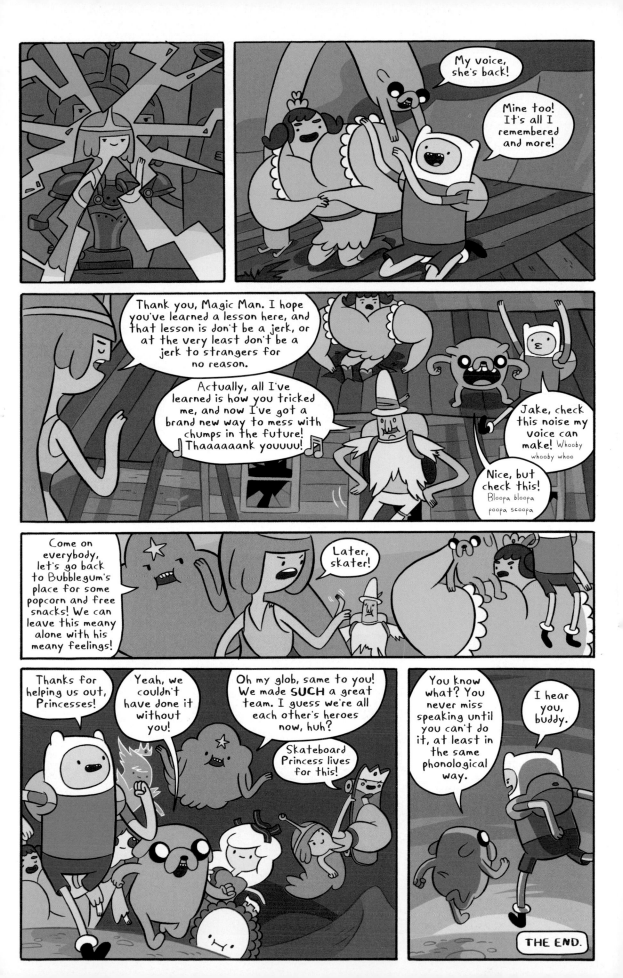

"Finally," I thought, "Finally, things are going to go my way. This is just the beginning. It's gonna be 100% different for me from now on."

BOOM

LUMPIN' FINALLY.

You okay, LSP?

Uh, I'm fabulous, Finn! I'm always fabulous, and you should know that about me by now! HONESTLY.

But I lumpin' want out now, okay?

Okay okay, just a sec! We had to beat up Ice King first.

Did you see? We had cool suits!!

I dunno why I chose her anyway. She's, like, my #1 least favorite princess by far.

"Least"?! THAT'S a super dumb way to pronounce "BEST ALL-TIME ULTIMATE FOREVER"!!

It's like--way off from how it's normally pronounced. Not even close, Ice King. You really dropped the ball on this one, I gotta say.

So you guys wanna go through this dungeon with me?

WITH you? I thought you said it was ultimate heroes only!

Well I mean normally it's heroes only, but I'm sure there'd be no trouble with you two tagging along with me.

Are you kidding, Jake? I don't **KIDNAP** princesses, guys! I rescue 'em.

From what?

Ha!

...You're serious?

Wait. Ice King, you...think you're a hero?

Ha ha! Right, because I'm **TOTALLY** the bad guy. Good one, Finn! You're a funny guy, you know that?

YOU KIDNAP PRINCESSES!!

"The lot in life of a princess is a sad one, guys. She's destined from birth to be trapped in the boring, tedious role of a head of state. Believe me, I know how it is!"

"Oh, the endless meetings! The infinite series of petty disputes all needing **YOUR** personal intervention! Those dang flippin' spurns that patient merit of the unworthy takes!"

"But don't princesses **DESERVE** only the best things in life? What if--like **YOU**, Jake--she wants excitement? What if--like **YOU**, Finn--she wants adventure?

"What if, like me, she even wants... COMPANIONSHIP??"

"I rescue princesses from boredom, guys! From loneliness! I rescue them from not having **ME** in their lives!"

Save me, Ice King!! Also I lumpin' love you or whatever!

In the script these panels are described as "Ice King-O-Vision." Which is also the name of a brand of ice glasses I'd wear in a heartbeat.

THEY DECORATED THEM REAL NICE, YOU DON'T EVEN KNOW.

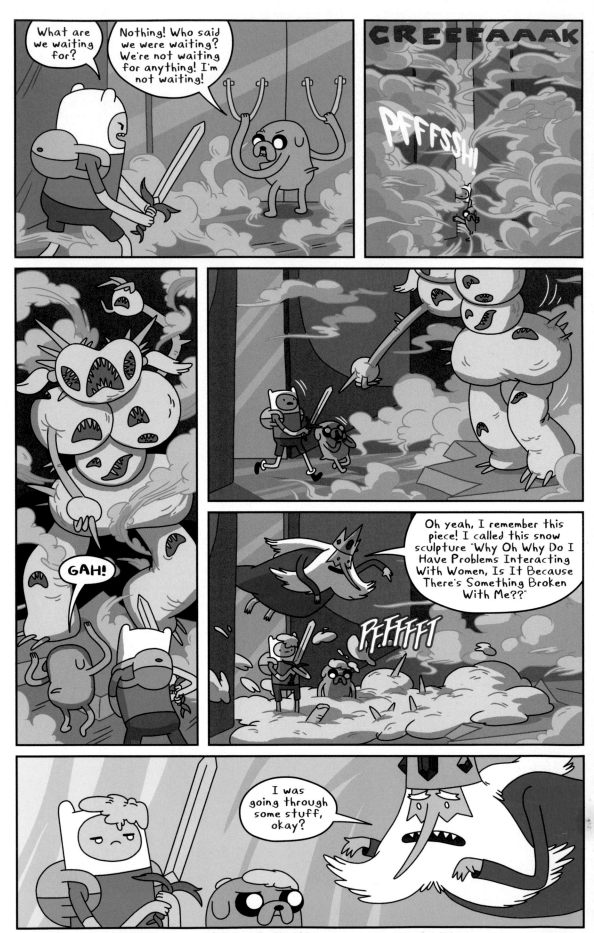

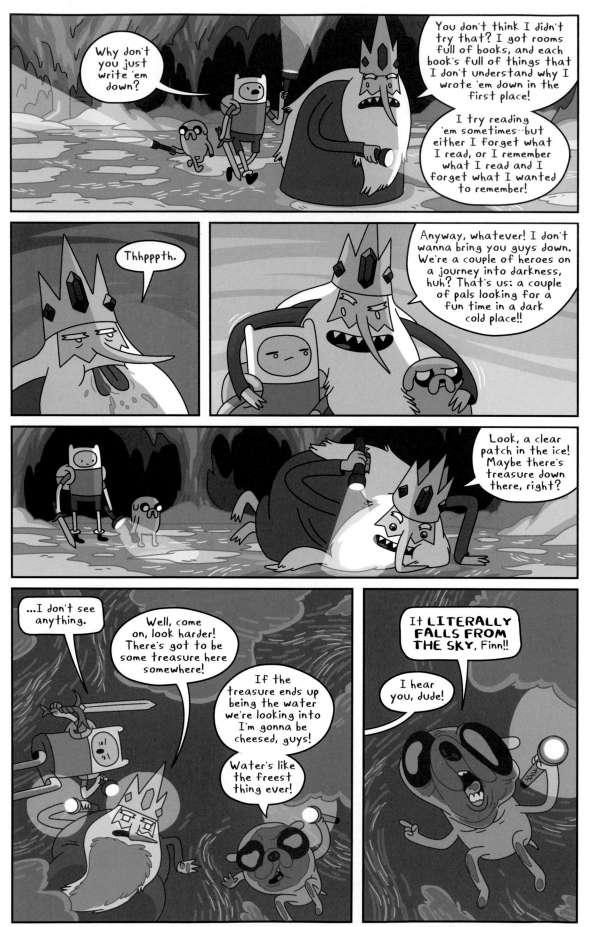

FINN: you will get covered in gross guts twice in one day. So, um, try to act surprised?

JAKE: an unexpected revelation unlocks an ancient secret which has the power to destroy the planet. DON'T MESS THIS UP DUDE.

LEMONGRAB: Okay sir--SIR. please. if you'll just--SIR. SIR. you need to CALM DOWN.

do do do de, do do do de, DO DO DO DE, DO DO DO DE DO DO DO DE DO DO DO DE....dah dah dah DAAAAH

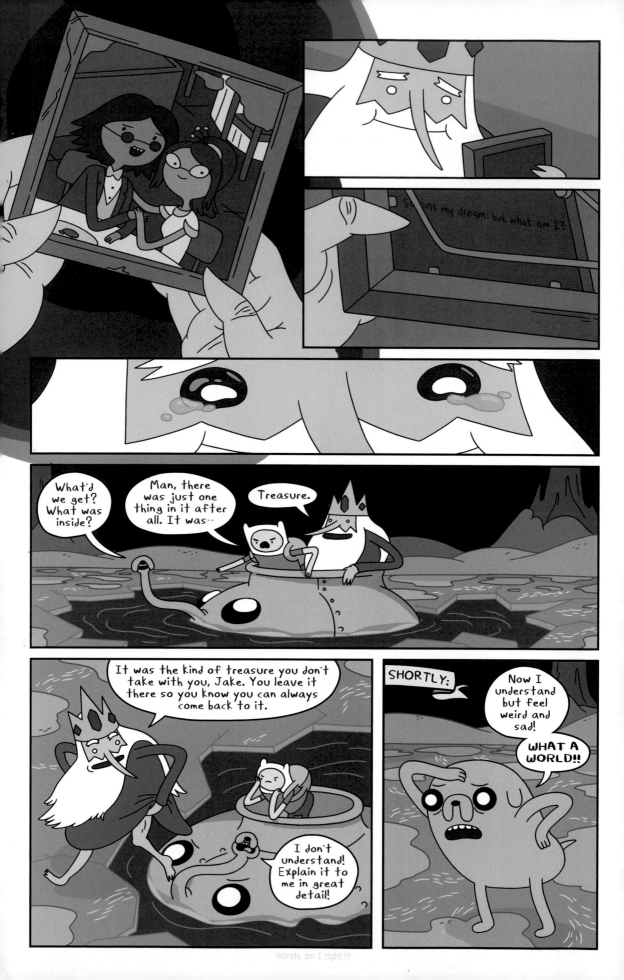

So runs my dream; but what am I?

What'd we get? What was inside?

Man, there was just one thing in it after all. It was—

Treasure.

It was the kind of treasure you don't take with you, Jake. You leave it there so you know you can always come back to it.

I don't understand! Explain it to me in great detail!

SHORTLY:

Now I understand but feel weird and sad!

WHAT A WORLD!!

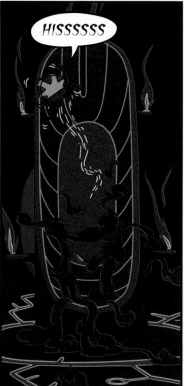

EVERYONE'S FIRST DUNGEON IS A LEARNING EXPERIENCE. COME ON GUYS, I THOUGHT THIS WAS UNDERSTOOD

HOOK CROOK
(GROSS-NASTY MODE)
ANCIENT UNKNOWABLE EVIL

OOOF!

JAKE!!

CHKK
CHHHHK

Jake! Help me out here!!

JAKE!

Blehhh

Alright mister, you've knocked out my best friend. You've knocked out the weird old man I hang out with. And now you've made me **MAD**.

CHHKH
CHKCCK
CHKKKK

There's just one thing to do. Mister, I am going to--

CONTINUED
NEXT CHAPTER

Oh wow. sorry. we got cut off there! Well. what was supposed to happen in panel six was--*SECRET TEXT ALSO CONTINUED NEXT CHAPTER*

Behold, we know not anything;
I can but trust that good shall fall
At last—far off—at last, to all,
And every winter change to spring.

So runs my dream: but what am I?

And with no language but a cry.

I had such high hopes for it too!

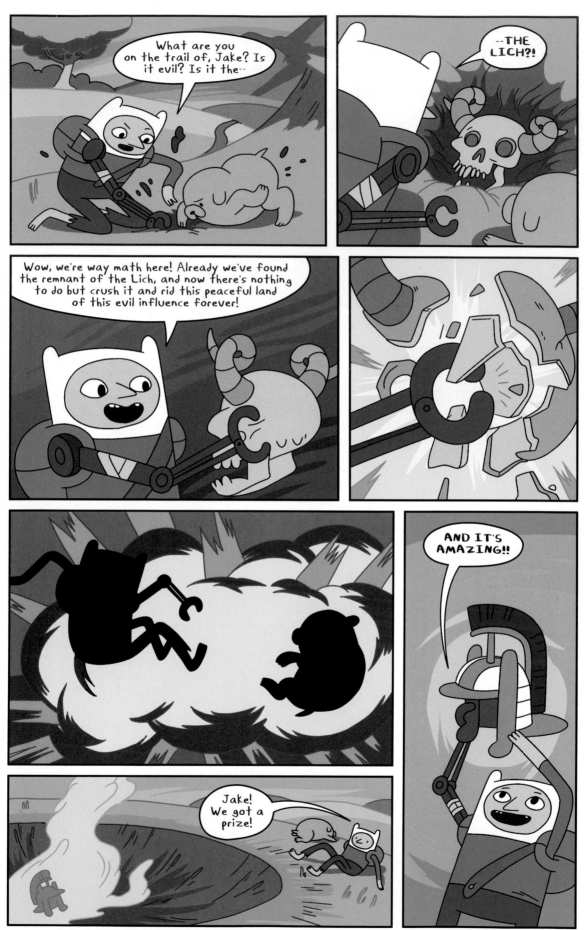

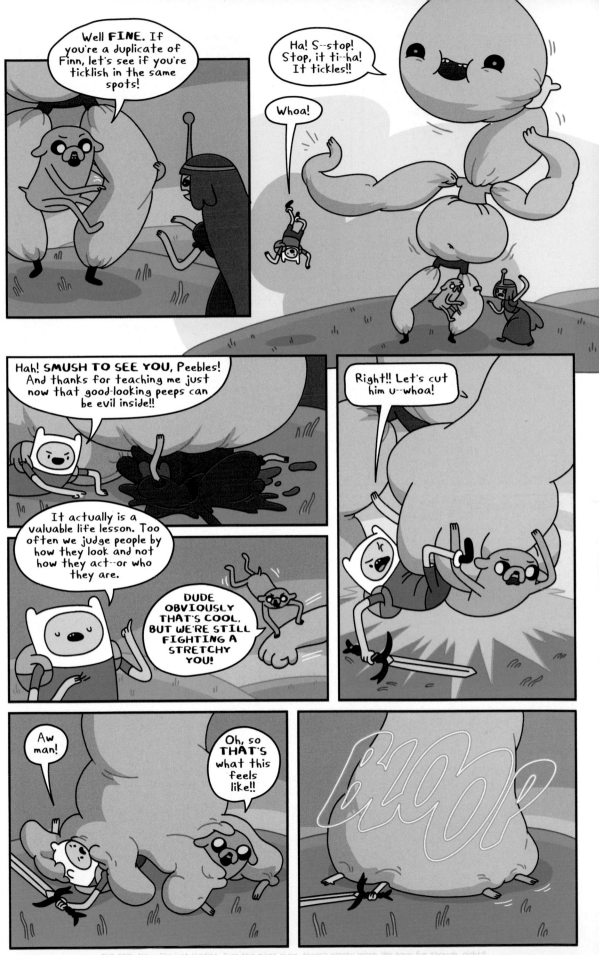

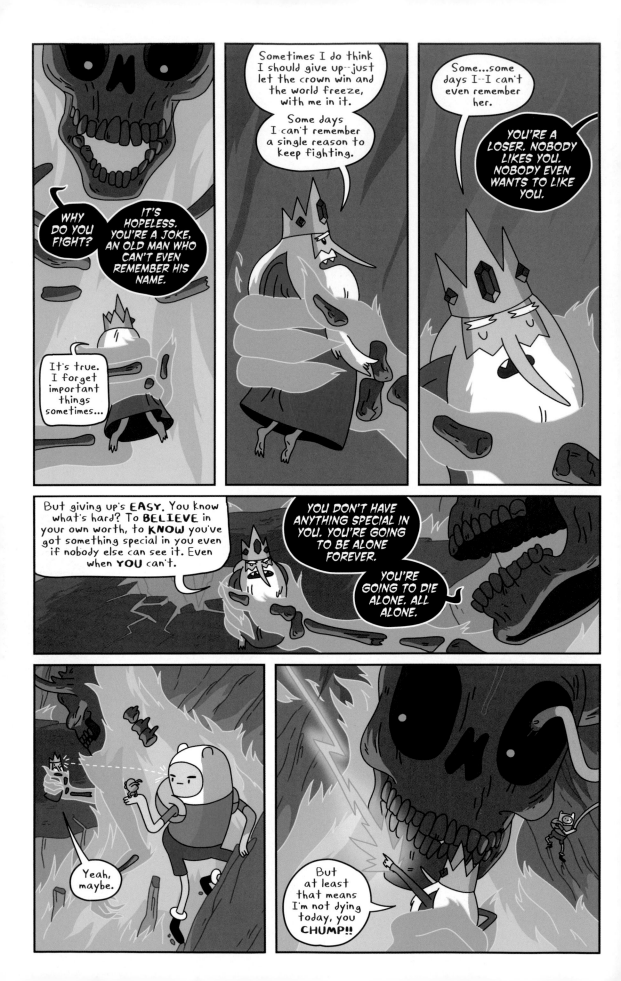

Cover 15B:
Emily Warren

EMILY
WARREN

MIKE
HOLMES.
PROPS TO P.T.!

Cover 16C:
Sophie Goldstein

Sophie
Goldstein

Cover 16D:
Meredith McClaren

Cover 17B:
Erika Moen

Cover 17C:
Jemma Salume

Cover 17D:
Meredith McClaren

Mondo Exclusive:
JJ Harrison

MIKE
HOLMES.

Cover 18B:
Kelly Bastow

Cover 18C:
Caroline Breault

Cover 18D:
Yehudi Mercado

CBLDF Exclusive:
Chrystin Garland

Cover 19B:
Britt Sanders

Cover 19C:
Matt Sheean

Cover 19D:
Chris Visions